BACKSTREET BOYS

WISE PUBLICATIONS
London / New York / Sydney / Paris / Copenhagen / Madrid

Exclusive Distributors: Music Sales Limited, 8/9 Frith Street, London W1V 5TZ, England • Music Sales Pty Limited, 120 Rothschild Avenue, Rosebery, NSW 2018, Australia

Order No. AM950664 • ISBN 0-7119-7044-0 • This book © Copyright 1997 by Wise Publications • Visit the Internet Music Shop at http://www.musicsales.co.uk

Unauthorised reproduction of any part of this publication by any means including photocopying is an infringement of copyright • Music arranged by Derek Jones

Music processed by Paul Ewers Music Design • Printed in the United Kingdom by Caligraving Limited, Thetford, Norfolk

Your Guarantee of Quality: As publishers, we strive to produce every book to the highest commercial standards • The music has been freshly engraved and, whilst endeavouring to retain the original running order of the recorded album, the book has been carefully designed to minimise awkward page turns and to make playing from it a real pleasure • Particular care has been given to specifying acid-free, neutral-sized paper made from pulps which have not been elemental chlorine bleached This pulp is from farmed sustainable forests and was produced with special regard for the environment • Throughout, the printing and binding have been planned to ensure a sturdy, attractive publication which should give years of enjoyment • If your copy fails to meet our high standards, please inform us and we will gladly replace it

Music Sales' complete catalogue describes thousands of titles and is available in full colour sections by subject, direct from Music Sales Limited

Please state your areas of interest and send a cheque/postal order for £1.50 for postage to: Music Sales Limited, Newmarket Road, Bury St. Edmunds, Suffolk IP33 3YB

NICK CARTER

ALEXANDER JAMES "A.J." MCLEAN

HOWARD "HOWIE D." DOROUGH

BRIAN "B-ROK." LITTRELL

KEVIN RICHARDSON

Everybody (Backstreet's Back)

WORDS & MUSIC BY DENNIZ POP & MAX MARTIN

Verse 2:
Now throw your hands up in the air
And wave 'em around like you just don't care
If you wanna party let me hear you yell
'Cos we got it going on again.

Am I original …

All I Have To Give

WORDS & MUSIC BY FULL FORCE

♩ = 96

1. I don't know____

____ what he does____ to make you cry, but I'll be there to make you smile.____

(Verse 2 see block lyric)

____ I don't have____ a fan-cy car____ to get to you, I'd

Verse 2:

When you talk does it seem like he's not
Even listening to a word you say?
That's okay babe, just tell me your problems
I'll try my best to kiss them all away
Does he leave when you need him the most?
Does his friends get all your time?
Baby please – I'm on my knees
Praying for the day that you'll be mine

But my love is all I have to give *etc.*

As Long As You Love Me

WORDS & MUSIC BY MAX MARTIN

Verse 2:
Every little thing that you have said and done
Feels like it's deep within me
Doesn't really matter if you're on the run
It seems like we're meant to be.

I don't care *etc.*

That's The Way I Like It

WORDS & MUSIC BY DENNIZ POP, MAX MARTIN & HERBERT CRICHLOW

Hey! _____ (That's the way I like it ba - by, that's the way I) That's the way I like it. (That's the way I like it ba - by, that's the way I, that's the way I like it.)

N.C.

1. Some-bo-dy told me that you're not my— kind— so have I lost my— mind.—
(Verse 2 see block lyric)

(That's the way I like it.) You keep on do-in' all the things I— like— you've got me

hyp - no - tized,———— but that's the way I like it.

Tacet 2°

Cm

B♭

Girl you make me wan - na move, it's the price I've got— to pay

for all the things you do girl I like it. Yeah now lis-ten to the groove

and you got-ta lis-ten well the way you're go-ing that's the way I like it.

Ev-'ry-bo-dy now, I like it. Ev-'ry-bo-dy now,

that's the way I like it. Ev-'ry-bo-dy come on, I like it.

26

Verse 2:
Oh mystery lady you got somethin' I like
Tell me you're here to stay
You're dangerous so baby could you do me right?
Will you come out to play?
'Cos that's the way I like it.

Gotta listen to the groove *etc.*

10,000 Promises

WORDS & MUSIC BY MAX MARTIN

Once we were lov-ers, lov-ers we were, all, all a lie.

Once we were dream-ers, dream-ers we were,— oh— you and I.—

you___ pro - mised___ me.___

Once I could han - dle the truth when the truth___ was___ you and I.___

But time af - ter time all the pro - mis - es turned___ out___ to

be all lies.___ Now,___ now I see I'm just some -

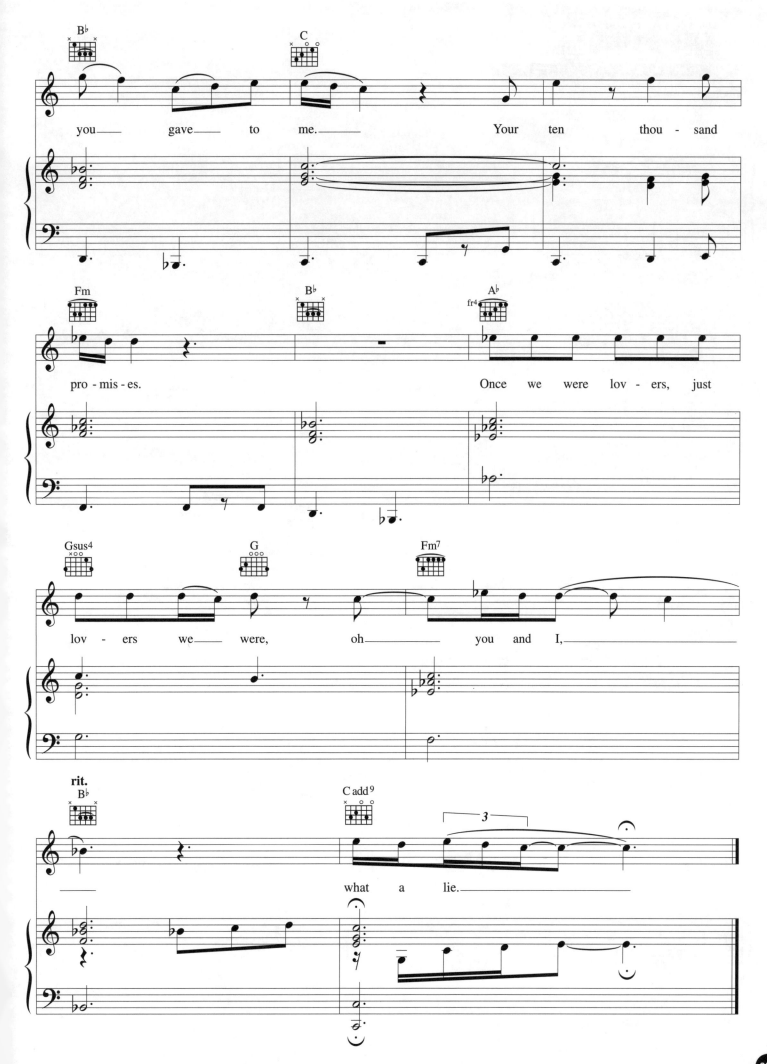

Like A Child

WORDS & MUSIC BY FITZGERALD SCOTT

If I could right the wrongs that made you cry

I'll make a pro - mise not to say good - night.

break down and cry— just like a child.———————— Like a child,— just like a child—

———————— with her spi - rits run - nin' free— she showed me why,—

———— oh she did, like a child,— just like a child.— Think of what—

—— our love— could be— if our hearts could set— us free— like a child.————————

Hey, Mr. DJ (Keep Playin' This Song)

WORDS & MUSIC BY TIMMY ALLEN, LARRY CAMPBELL & JOLYON SKINNER

Verse 2:
Now it feels like it could be romance
As we dance across the floor
Every move that your body makes
Only makes me want you more.
And it seems like time's moving fast
How can we make it last
Make it last somehow.

As you keep on dancing
I am hypnotized *etc.*

Set Adrift On Memory Bliss

WORDS & MUSIC BY ATTRELL CORDES & GARY KEMP

Da da da da da da da da da da da da da da da da da da da da da da.

1. The cam-era pans the hour glass, the days go and all I do is

Verse 3:
Sadness, it overwhelms me
My mind flies and carelessly
Imagines that you're happy
With your life right now.
I guess that's just the way it goes
Forever's gone so now I must place you
With all the things that I can never have.

Baby you set me *etc.*

That's What She Said

WORDS & MUSIC BY BRIAN LITTRELL

Do do do dee do do do do do do.___ Yeah yeah yeah yeah yeah.___ Mm.

1. There are peo - ple   say what you wan - na hear,   ev - en on a rain - y day they'll

(Verse 2 see block lyric)

Verse 2:
And there are people say what they really mean
She said she'd always be there
She said she'd always care
But just when you think that you can
Trust that someone you love
Tell me why, do you know
How stars can fall from above

Always forever *etc.*

If You Want It To Be Good Girl (Get Yourself A Bad Boy)

WORDS & MUSIC BY ROBERT JOHN 'MUTT' LANGE

Oh yeah. And if you wan - na get it done babe you got - ta get the one, the one who's got it go - in' on. If you wan - na make it last, got - ta know just who to ask, babe he's got - ta be the best. If you

wan-na show you how._____ So won't you let me show you right now, oh ba - by.

And you,— yes.

And_____ if you wan-na get it done babe, you got-ta get__ the one,__ the one__

who's got it go - in' on._____ If you wan - na make it last got - ta

Repeat to fade

Verse 2:
If you like it innovative
Better get someone creative honey
And if you want it to be jammin'
You've gotta get somebody slammin' baby

And if you wanna get it done babe *etc.*

If I Don't Have You

WORDS & MUSIC BY GARY BAKER, WAYNE PERRY & TIMMY ALLEN

1. Ev - 'ry day girl I wake up and___
(Verse 2 see block lyric)

pray___ that you'll come back___ home,_____ and don't take too long._____

'Cos since you've been___ gone ev - 'ry-thing's go - o - ing___

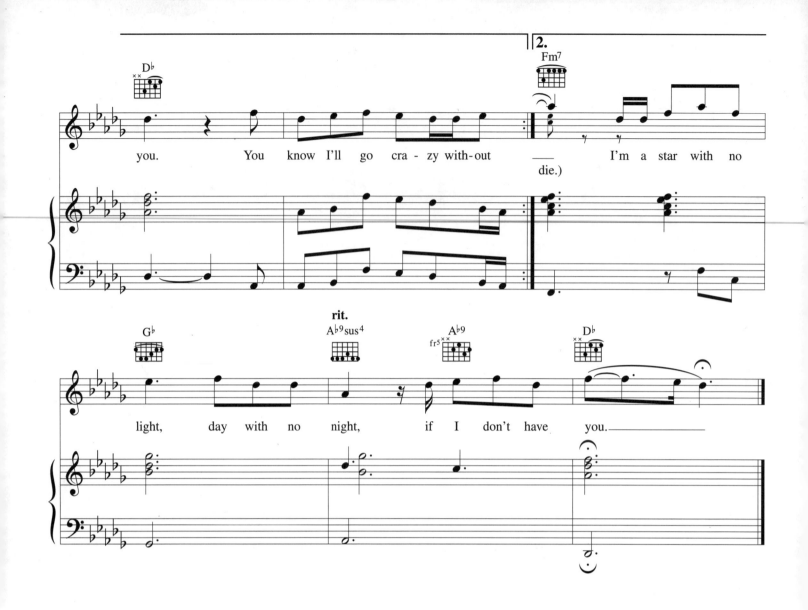

Verse 2:
Late at night I reach to hold you tight
But you're not there
I know you still care
And oh how I miss your soft and love, lovely kiss
You give to me
Sentimentally
We used to feel time would stand still
When I see you baby you will
So hurry home
You know your man needs you so.

If I don't have you *etc.*

6/98 (31078)